The "FOREVER FRIENDS" · Bear Book ·

· by Deborah Jones ·

First published in 1993
by Brownsword Books
28 Gay Street, Bath, England

Printed and bound in Great Britain by
William Clowes Limited, Beccles and London

ISBN 1 873615 10 8

To Tracy

Love from Julie
xxxx

i am a much Loved Bear
.... all soft and cuddlesome ....

.... i have big fluffy ears,
you can tell me all your
Secrets ......

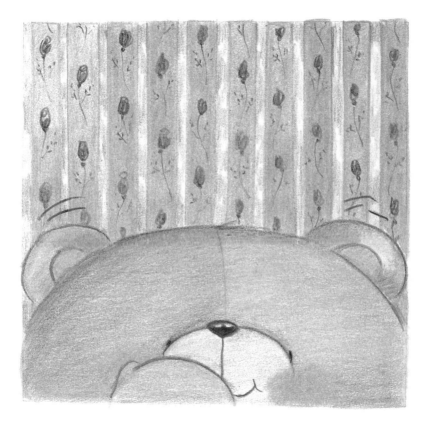

....and i will never tell
a soul.

....i will go everywhere with you....

.... and when you have to go away alone, i will always be there to welcome you home!

... i will forgive you <u>any</u>thing!

....My heart is golden,
like my fur.

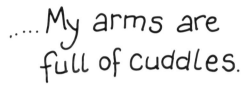

..... My arms are
full of cuddles.

When no one else seems
to care ....

...you can always
rely on your Bear !

....when i get Old and Scruffy i am all the better to Hug!

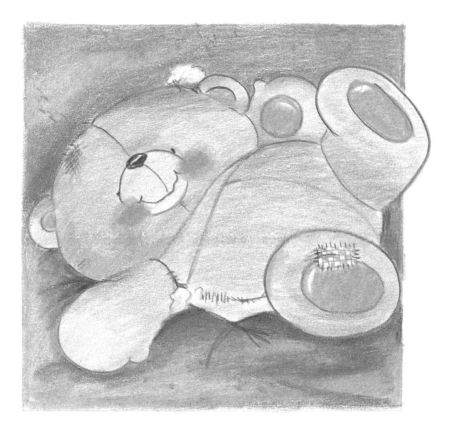

...your smile makes me smile....

...you are my Forever Friend!

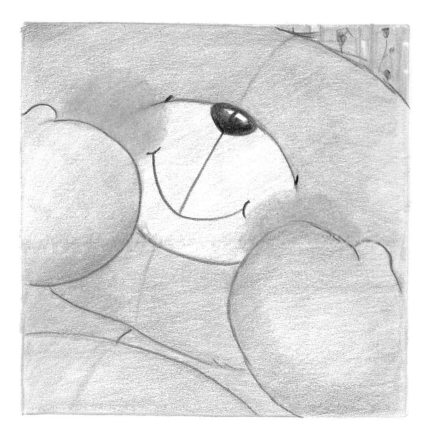